RESOURCES

OLLEGE

What's wrong with me?

The ACE project
'Literacy for Active Citizenship' series

Written by Lee Yoon Teng
Illustrated by Karen Dudley

What's wrong with me?
© Learning Unlimited 2015

Published by Learning Unlimited Ltd as part of the Active Citizenship and English (ACE) project. The ACE project, led by Learning Unlimited, was funded through the European Integration Fund and delivered in partnership with Blackfriars Settlement, Working Men's College and the UCL Institute of Education.

Foreword

The ACE project
'Literacy for Active Citizenship' series

The Active Citizenship and English (ACE) project, led by Learning Unlimited and delivered in partnership with Blackfriars Settlement, Working Men's College and the UCL Institute of Education, received funding from the European Integration Fund (July 2013 to June 2015).

The ACE project aimed to support non-EU women to develop their skills and confidence in English and to take an active part in everyday life in the UK. As part of the project we wanted to produce a series of readers for our learners, and other adults also settling in the UK, which include stories about funny, personal and less typical aspects of everyday life in the UK. These stories were written by learners and volunteer befrienders on the ACE project and edited by ESOL specialists at Learning Unlimited. The supporting activities were also developed by the Learning Unlimited team.

We hope you enjoy using the 'Literacy for Active Citizenship' series.

To find out more about the ACE project, please see:
www.learningunlimited.co/projects/ace

Ja Yong is 50 years old. He always thought he was 'young' but now he has started to feel old and tired. When he gets home, he just wants to sleep.
"I don't know why I'm so tired and I want to sleep all the time. I'm not old, am I?" he asks himself.

Until recently, Ja Yong had an office job at Transport for London. He went to work every morning at 7.30 am and got home by 6 pm. He never arrived home late but when he got home, he always felt too tired to do anything.

"I'm not that old. I'm a strong man. What's wrong with me? Why am I always thirsty and tired?" he said to himself. "Never mind. If I don't think about it, it will get better."

One day, Ja Yong was offered promotion. He was very happy but he needed to have a medical check-up for the new job. He was worried about this because he felt so tired and thirsty. He booked an appointment with his GP for the medical check-up.

On the appointment day, Ja Yong arrived at the surgery. He paced nervously up and down outside. The receptionist told him the doctor was waiting for him.

"How is your general health?" the doctor asked him. "Very good, thank you," replied Ja Yong. The doctor asked him lots more questions. Then she measured him, weighed him, took his blood pressure and did a blood test.

"Your blood pressure is high," the doctor told him.

Two weeks later, Ja Yong got a call from the surgery. "Hello Mr Ja, can you come to the surgery tomorrow morning to have another blood test? Please don't eat or drink anything before you come."

Ja Yong was very worried and that night he couldn't sleep. He imagined he was dying and all his family were crying.

Ja Yong went for the second blood test. For the next week, Ja Yong was more and more worried. He was grumpy and angry with everyone. He didn't want to tell his family why he was worried.

A week later, Ja Yong had another call from the surgery, "You need to make an appointment to see the doctor as soon as possible," the receptionist told him. Ja Yong made an appointment for the next day. Now he was very, very worried.

The next day, Ja Yong went to the surgery. "Good morning, Mr Ja. Your results show that you are borderline diabetic. At this stage, you don't need to take any medication but you must change your diet," the doctor told him.

"Every day you have to exercise, eat some fresh fruit and lots of vegetables. Don't eat any sugar. This will help you to become healthier. I want you to come back and see me in two months' time. Here's a list of what to eat and what food you must avoid," she said.

He went home and showed the list to his wife. "Ah ha! No more cake and chocolate for you!" said his wife. "Why don't you go and see the Chinese herbalist too? They will give you some tea to drink."

Ja Yong now walks to work instead of taking the bus. He eats lots of vegetables and some fruit every day. He misses eating biscuits and chocolates but now he is much happier. His blood pressure is normal and he feels younger and more energetic again.

Key words

borderline	nearly
diabetic	when your body does not produce enough insulin (a hormone made by the body)
diet	what you eat
grumpy	in a bad mood
imagines	thinks
herbalist	someone who makes medicine using plants
medication	medicine
never mind	don't worry
nervously	showing that you are worried
paces	walks up and down

Questions

1. How did Ja Yong feel before he visited the doctor?

2. What was Ja Yong's job?

3. How did Ja Yong feel when he got home?

4. Why was Ja Yong worried about going to the doctor?

5. Did Ja Yong tell the doctor he did not feel well? Why not?

6. Before his second blood test, what did Ja Yong imagine?

7. What did the GP tell Ja Yong he must do?

8. What did Ja Yong's wife tell him to do?

9. How did Ja Yong feel when he stopped eating food with sugar and he started to exercise?

Activity 1 - Role play

In pairs, role play one of the following:

Role play 1: The conversation between Ja Yong and the doctor when the doctor tells him he is borderline diabetic.

Ja Yong: Remember to ask the doctor some questions.

Doctor: Remember to tell Ja Yong what he must do.

Role play 2: The conversation between Ja Yong and his wife when he comes home after the doctor has told him he is borderline diabetic.

Ja Yong: Tell your wife how worried you were. You also need to tell her what borderline diabetic means.

Wife: Ask Ja Yong about what the doctor says and give him some advice.

Activity 2 - Healthy menu

Write a menu for a healthy lunch for some special guests including Ja Yong.

Activity 3 - Recipes

Write a recipe for one of the dishes you included in your special healthy meal.
Below are some words you might find useful:

First	then	after that
next	when	boil
fry	steam	chop
peel	stir	add

For downloadable activities, visit:
www.learningunlimited.co/resources/publications

Acknowledgements

What's wrong with me? was written by Lee Yoon Teng and illustrated by Karen Dudley. We are grateful to them for being able to include their work as part of the 'Literacy for Active Citizenship' series.